CHRISTAL

Coping with Spina Bifida

by
Karen Snyder Travis

BRANDEN BOOKS
Boston

Library of Congress Cataloging-in-Publication Data

Travis, Karen Snyder.
　　Christal: coping with spina bifida /
　　by Karen Snyder Travis.
　　　　p.; cm.
　　Includes bibliographical references.
　　ISBN 0-8283-2062-4
　　1. Travis, Christal, 1983- 2. Spina bifida--Patients--
Biography. I. Title: Coping with spina bifida. 　　II. Title.
　　　　[DNLM: 1. Travis, Christal, 1983-2. 2. Spinal
Dysraphism--psychology--PersonalNarratives.3. Family--
psychology--Personal　Narratives. WE 730 T782c 2001]
　　RJ496.S74 T737 2001
　　362.1'989283--dc21
　　[B]　　　　　　　　　　　　　　　2001018411

BRANDEN BOOKS
(Division of Branden Publishing Co.)
PO Box 812094
Wellesley MA 02482

CONTENTS

1. September, 1983
BIRTH OF CHRISTAL

We had just moved to Northern Florida, to a little town called Branford, when I became pregnant with Christal. Christal's father, Tom, had transferred within the company he worked, but was unable to keep the same insurance. Because we were unable to afford an obstetrician, we were forced to use the county clinic. This turned out to be a blessing for Christal.

The pregnancy was a normal one for me. I never experienced morning sickness with any of my children, and I gained only the amount of weight I was supposed to. The only complication I had was a kidney infection, which developed when I was five months pregnant. I was hospitalized for one week.

One week before my due date I had an appointment with the clinic. The doctor informed me that my baby was in the breech position, and that the placenta was in front of the baby, which would prevent the use of forceps.

"The baby will have to turn around this week or we will have to perform a cesarean," his words still echoed in my ears as I felt the first contraction at home a few days later.

I looked at the clock on the living room wall to time the distance between contractions. My first child was born in only six and one half hours, so I expected this baby to also be born quickly. And since we lived roughly forty-five miles from the hospital, time was an important factor.

The second contraction was only five minutes from the first!

"This must be wrong," I thought, so I watched for the next contraction, which was only three minutes from the second! I needed to get Tom home and quick.

Tom worked at a lime rock quarry driving heavy equipment. We also lived in a trailer on the site. It was our responsibility to watch over the five hundred acre business in exchange for housing.

I could hear someone driving behind our trailer on heavy equipment, so I quickly went to the back door and threw it open just as Tom was driving by on a pay loader.

How Tom heard my scream I'll never know. Heavy equipment is very loud. But I pointed to my belly, and he jumped off the pay loader.

"We have to go, the contractions are only three minutes apart." I was really starting to worry.

We gathered my things and got in the car. Tom drove through every red light, horn blaring. We were doing between ninety and one hundred miles per hour all the way there. I was worried that our nineteen seventy-four Maverick would not survive the trip. Then, about half way there I started to get the urge to push.

"Hurry Tom", I said, "I'm having pushing pains."

"Don't breathe like that" he told me. I was holding my breath. "Take short breaths", he said.

I did, and it helped. I don't know how he knew what to do. I wanted to take Lamaze classes with him but he didn't want any part of the delivery room.

"A father's place is in the waiting room," he said.

I don't think he wanted to see me going through any pain. So, I read books on the Lamaze technique. Only it didn't do me any good without Tom telling me what to do. Anyway, it kept the baby from being born on Interstate 75.

Our car squealed into the Emergency Entrance of the Hospital, and Tom jumped out. Within seconds the emergency room staff pushed me on a bed and took me immediately into an elevator, while Tom went back to park the car. Everything happened so fast, I wondered if anyone had told Tom where I had been taken.

Fear crept over me again as I remembered what the doctor had told me earlier in the week. I am deathly afraid of pain.

"Your going to give me something to put me asleep, aren't you" I pleaded? "I don't want to be awake when they cut me".

"Your not having a cesarean, your already having this baby naturally", the doctor, stated.

I was too far along in labor to have drugs. When you are in enough pain, you don't care what is happening or what anyone thinks, you want the pain too stop. But Christal was born, and the pain did not last as long as the previous delivery with her sister.

The hospital staff must have given me something almost immediately after the delivery because I didn't remember anything that happened after she was born, until they had cleaned both of us.

A nurse wheeled her bed next to mine. I thought it strange that she lay on a normal size bed. She had two very large pieces of cotton in her little eyes. I was very groggy, but I remember the doctor telling me Christal Marie was born with a birth defect. She would need more care, and that I could see her later.

Christal Marie, what a perfect name, I thought. Who had named her? Had I named her when I was groggy? Even the nurses were calling her Christal Marie. Tom and I had been so sure she was a boy that we didn't even pick out a girl's name. Deep in my heart I had wanted another girl though. I figured God must have named her, and so we spell her name like Christ with an "al" at the end...Christal.

I was then taken to an operating room. Everything was still difficult for me to understand. There was a problem with the placenta. All of it did not come out during delivery, and the doctor would have to perform a DNC.

"What is a DNC?" I thought about this for two seconds, and then everything was black.

I woke up in a very small room, about the size of a closet. The nurse who was in there with me told me they called it the recovery room. At the age of twenty-one I just didn't know much about anything except being a young mother and wife. It would take weeks for me to grasp all that had taken place.

Finally a familiar face, Tom had walked in. The nurse left us alone. We talked I'm sure, but I was still groggy from the drugs they had given me. Then a doctor came in. He was short and had black hair. He told us that our baby was very sick, and would probably die. If she did live, she would be paralyzed from the neck down and would be severely mentally retarded. He advised us that it would be better for Christal to let her die. But, we did have a choice between doing nothing and letting them operate.

He left and another doctor came in--Dr. Hutchinson. He had a Scottish accent. He was a very warm and friendly man with a Scottish accent. He told us that Christal was born with Spina Bifida, a birth defect where the spinal cord and spine do not develop correctly. Christal's spinal cord was exposed in a sack outside her back. This sack had been punctured during birth. They needed to operate on her immediately to reduce the risk of spinal meningitis. He left us with a lot of hope that Christal could, and more than likely, would live with this operation.

All these big words I had never heard before. It really didn't matter to me what Christal was born with. Tom and I looked at each other and we knew that whatever had to be done, we wanted them to do it. She was our baby, a gift from God. You don't turn your back on your own flesh and blood. I loved her from the minute I first saw her, no matter what problems she had, I always would.

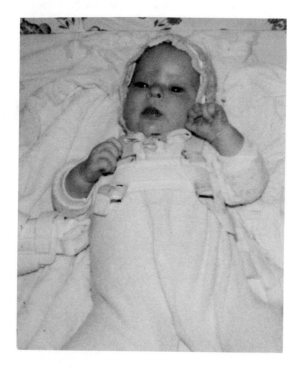

1. Christal in hip braces--4 months old.

2. Early Treatment
1ST MAJOR SURGERY

Within an hour after she was born, Christal underwent major surgery. They had to connect all the nerves in the spinal column to their various organs and muscles. She would be in surgery for a while.

I was taken out of the recovery room and placed in the maternity ward. I aged ten years that day, and so did her father, I'm sure. We had a thousand questions. No one we knew had ever heard of Spina Bifida. How did our baby get this birth defect? Neither of us took drugs or drank alcohol. I never smoked cigarettes, and Tom never smoked around me when I was pregnant. What had we done wrong?

We were briefed by the doctor on Christal's condition, and were told where she was. It was very hard for me to remember all that they told us, because I didn't even understand most of what they were saying, and I was somewhat numb emotionally. Finally, we were taken to a room where we were asked to wash our hands and put on a hospital gown over our clothes. Then we were taken into an area called NICU (neo-natal intensive care unit).

There were, it seemed, twenty little incubator beds with a tiny little baby in each. I noticed another couple who were visiting their premature baby. They were about our age, I thought. And there was Christal. She was lying on her belly, and her legs were sticking straight out, as if they would not bend. And her butt stuck up a bit. I asked the nurse what was wrong with her legs? She told me that Christal had held this position inside me, and eventually her legs would relax. She had a very large bandage on her back, which covered up her surgery. She was tiny to us, but was of normal size and looked very large compared to all the other babies in the unit.

Each baby had its own nurse, and Christal's was very nice. They all were. I always thought nurses were mean and delivered pain, but not here. We weren't allowed to stay long, but we could come back at all visiting hours, which we did, gladly. It almost seemed as though she was the hospital's baby, and we were permitted to visit. I had to develop thick skin, for I knew Christal would need all the strength I could give her. I was determined not to cry or show weakness in front of her.

The hospital took advantage of the time we would have away from Christal to help get us grants to pay for the operations and hospital stay. They also educated us on Spina Bifida, and taught us to care for her when the time came to take her home. We were advised that she would need a lot more care in the future, that she would probably develop hydro-cephalus (fluid built up on the brain), which would require another operation to install a shunt (pump). We were given a shunt to look at and feel. I found it amazing that the father of a child with Spina Bifida, an engineer, had invented the pump portion of this little medical tool. This shunt was suppose to re-route the spinal fluid so that it would not build up and put pressure on the brain. It required no manual pumping and could easily be fit into the palm of my hand.

2. Christal, three months old.

3. Separation
WITHOUT CHRISTAL

I was released from the hospital a few days after Christal was born. It was very hard leaving her there overnight, but I also had to rest. The DNC, I had, was hard on my body, and the doctors warned me not to overlook my own health.

I cried all the way home. Christal was my second child, and both times I had to go home without my baby. This was very difficult for me. There definitely is something to be said for the mother-to-child bond from both points of view.

Tom got a week off from work, and we would need it to be able to go back and forth to the hospital every day. We left our other daughter, Elizabeth, with Tom's sister, Debbie. I hated leaving my children with anyone but I knew Debbie would take just as good of care, if not better, than I could give her now.

Early every morning we would leave for the hospital, and would not return until late every evening. This was also a financial strain on us with which we had been struggling.

One day as we were leaving, we saw the couple that had a premature baby in the same room with Christal. They were crying on the steps of the hospital. I found out the next day that their baby had died. I thanked God for the work he was doing in Christal's life, and begged him to continue to watch over her. My heart ached for that couple that could have easily been us.

Christal's legs were straightening out as the doctor had said they would. She looked like a normal baby to me. If all went well she would be able to go home after two weeks, provided that she did not develop hydrocephalus. Because of the weak spot in her spine, there was the possibility that a blockage could occur in the normal route that the ventricular fluid would take, resulting in a build up on the brain, which would cause pressure and would lead to death. The doctors had told us that she did not have this problem as of yet. Although only five percent of the children born with Spina Bifida never get it, they were pretty sure Christal eventually would, and it would be better to catch it in the hospital than after she was released.

4. The Shunt
2ND MAJOR SURGERY

S hands Hospital is part of the University of Florida. Christal was born just before the homecoming football game. On one occasion while visiting with Christal, the nurses had knitted all the babies in the nursery little hats in the university colors, orange and blue. Since most of the babies that they took care of were premature, it would make sense to make the hats small. But not for Christal. She was a normal size baby. I'll never forget the nurse trying to put a hat on her head. It was a nice thought, but it just wouldn't fit.

We had a hard time getting out of Gainesville that day. The city was packed with people there to see the game.

One evening after we were at home, one of Christal's doctors called. He was the resident pediatric neurologist, but I did not recognize his name. He explained that Christal would need to have the shunt, and he wanted us to see him that next morning.

Christal was already scheduled to have surgery, and he needed our consent.

I didn't accept the fact that he thought she needed the shunt. In my heart I felt she really didn't need it. I was crushed. I took this harder than when they told me that she had the birth defect. I think I just believed that God was not going to let anything else happen to her.

We met the doctor that next morning, he introduced himself as Dr. Mickle. He was to be a very special person in our hearts in the years to come. I did not realize it until he told us, but he had been the pediatric neurosurgeon who had operated on Christal one hour after she was born. I was to find out later that he was the main doctor in this field in the state of Florida at that time. God was taking care of Christal even before she was born. He made sure she was born in the best hospital in the state with the best doctor in the state to handle her birth defect.

Dr. Mickle told us that although the tests that they had done showed that Christal only had a slight build-up of fluid, he felt the safest way for Christal was to operate, and give her a shunt. He saw over two thousand Spina Bifida babies a year, and I believed that he knew what he was doing.

We went to see Christal before surgery. The nurses had already prepped her, and I could tell they did not want us to touch her. I wanted to kiss her before they took her in the elevator, but they would not let me. It was so hard watching her go.

The operation lasted four hours, and I cried the whole time. I had become very attached to her, as any mother would after only two weeks. Our families were all there and we tried to talk and watch television while Christal was gone. It was the longest day I've ever had in my life.

I was relieved when Dr. Mickle finally came back and told us the operation was over, and we would be able to see Christal in a little while. Everything went well, and as long as she did not develop spinal meningitis she would be fine.

They took her to the nursery. She had an IV in her arm. She had black and blue marks on her toes from being pricked for all the different times they had needed blood tests. In the week to follow she would look like a pincushion. On one occasion, I came in to find an IV in her head. This was too much for me, so I complained to Dr. Mickle. She had just gone through a major operation on her head, and the nurses had stuck an IV right next to the incision. Dr. Mickle had them move the IV.

"They never should have put it there in the first place" he said.

The next day on our visit we found Christal's bed empty. She had been moved to the newborn nursery.

"This is a good sign," I thought. "Maybe she would be coming home soon."

I had mixed emotions about this. I missed her and wanted her home. But I was a bit afraid I wouldn't be able to give her the care she needed. I wasn't even sure I knew what that was yet.

The newborn nursery turned out to be a disappointment. Christal did not receive the same treatment as before. The babies in here were normal and didn't require as much care. On one visit, while Christal was asleep, another baby started to cry. I offered to pick it up and give it a bottle, but the nurse would not let me. It was against hospital policy to let anyone touch someone else's baby. That poor little baby cried the entire time I was in there with Christal, about twenty-five minutes.

"You will just have to cry, because I'm on my break" the nurse informed the baby.

I'm sure the baby really understood what she was saying!

I was not just Christal's mother; I was her protector and her voice. On one visit to the newborn nursery, Christal felt a little too warm. I checked her temperature, and she had a fever of one hundred and one. The nurse had not even checked on her. The pediatrician on duty had to withdraw some of the fluid in her shunt just to rule out meningitis. This was enough for me. I talked to Dr. Mickle, and he had her moved to the seventh floor where the kept all the children who were sick.

5. Going Home
TRIP HOME

The day finally came for us to take Christal home. The orthopedic doctors fitted Christal with a brace, which kept her legs in a frog like position. This was supposed to keep the hipbones in their sockets to give the sockets time to grow around the bone. Christal needed this brace since both of her hips were dislocated. I was instructed how to put her in and take her out of them, and at what intervals it was to be done.

So there we were, finally going home with our baby three weeks and two operations after she was born. I made up my mind right then that no matter what Christal was going to have to go through I was not going to let her see one trace of fear or pain in my eyes. I was going to be strong for her, because I had to. We strapped Christal in the car seat, as best as we could with her brace on, and headed home.

Christal was a beautiful baby. Her hair was light brown, although it had been shaved on the side where her shunt was. She had dark brown eyes and an olive complexion like myself. She was a petite little girl, a little angel. She almost never cried except when she slept. And she slept with her eyes partially open for the first few weeks. I always thought that it was because she was always being wakened in the hospital for tests and etc., and the pain she must have endured, maybe she remembered it all when she slept.

I cared for her just like her sister before her. She was normal to me; whatever lay in the future was up to God to handle, and I knew He would. But my health had deteriorated and before the first week was over I was again back at Shand's hospital.

6. Back to the Hospital
MOM HOSPITALIZED

The DNC that had been performed on me was unsuccessful. I had lost so much blood that the nurse who checked my blood pressure told me to sit because he was afraid that I would pass out. They performed an emergency DNC on me.

Because it was to be done in the emergency room and not in the operating room, they were not able to put me to sleep. Consequently, the drugs I was given only numbed my brain and slowed down my muscle control, but it did little for the pain I was enduring. At one point during the procedure, I begged the doctor to stop just long enough for me to please get a breath and relax my muscles. The pain was excruciating.

The hospital kept me in intensive care for two days, and I remained in the hospital for a total of seven days, against my wishes.

"I have a newborn at home, and she requires a lot of special care", I pleaded.

But they would not release me and I was too weak too fight.

My mom came up to take care of my children and Tom until I was able to come home.

7. Orthotics
BRACES

Christal grew like most other children do, and as she grew we constantly made trips back and forth to Shands for bigger braces. When Christal was born her main doctors were neurologists. Once her neurological problems were taken care of, the orthopedic doctors replaced them, although we would still continue to see Dr. Mickle at every clinic appointment.

The main concern orthopedicaly was to keep Christal's hips in their sockets until the sockets had enough time to grow around them. This proved to be futile, and after a year and a half they gave up on it.

On one occasion, Christal was in an apparatus called a parapodium (a brace that holds the child's legs firmly in a stand up position). It had a base at the bottom, and the top wrapped around the waist. I always took my children wherever I went, no matter what brace Christal was in. We went to the grocery store. Christal was in her Para podium standing in the back of the cart, when the cashier rudely asked me what had I done to Christal. Normally I talk freely about Christal's birth defect, and I should have practiced a little restraint, but this girl was so shallow that I answered without thinking that I had pushed Christal down the stairs, "and here she is." I wondered if she actually believed me.

JANUARY, 1984

Tom and I purchased an old frame house, and had it moved to four acres of property in Live Oak, Florida, that we had purchased just before we moved to Branford. Live Oak is located just thirty miles away from Branford, and Tom's family lived there. We moved into our home as soon as the electricity and water were connected. This would make it easier for me to get Christal to physical therapy when the time came, because the therapist was located only twenty miles away from Live Oak. Christal's pediatrician, Dr. Brown, was also located in Live Oak.

3. Christal in parapodium, one year old.

8. Teething on her Toes
TOES

Christal grew almost like a normal child would. She learned to sit up, crawl and even to walk with the help of a small walker. It was obvious that her legs were weaker though. While her upper legs looked strong and muscular, her lower legs appeared thin and weak, and her feet seemed lifeless, in fact, she had little to no feeling in them at all.

One morning after I had awaken; I went into Christal's room to see if she was awake. I found Christal in her crib, playing with her toes. Her foot was covered with blood and so was her face. At first I did not know what had happened and I panicked. As I began to clean her up I discovered that she had chewed the entire nail and most of the skin off her big toe and the one next to it. Her pediatrician assured me that this was quite common in children with Spina Bifida. She was only experiencing what any other child her age would do only she had no feeling in her toes to tell her how hard to teeth on her toes. From this point on I would have to keep socks on her at night. Dr. Brown bandaged Christal up and explained to me that I would need to change the dressing on Christal's wounds. He also assured me that Christal's toenail would most likely grow back. It did.

One week later I was to take Christal back to Dr. Brown's office, so that he could check the progress of her wound. On the way to the doctors office Christal, who was sitting behind my seat in her car seat, got her sock off and started to chew again on the same toe. Fortunately, I caught her before she got the dressing off.

9. Odd Bacteria in her Blood
BACTERIA

From the moment Christal could voice her own opinion, it was obvious that she would be a strong-willed child. She not only knew what she wanted, she also knew how to go about getting it. I remember the way she would let me know which foods she did not like. She would just bite her gums together and absolutely not open her mouth unless it was something she wanted.

One afternoon, while I was getting ready to feed her lunch, she developed a fever of one hundred and six. I had just placed her in the high chair and went to get the food, when I looked at her again she was almost lethargic. Her forehead was on fire, and she was becoming listless. I gave her Tylenol and a bathed her in cold water to get the fever down. Then I raced her down to Dr. Brown's office. He saw her immediately and instructed me to take her to the county hospital, which was located next door, they would be expecting her, and he would be over shortly.

My mother and I walked her over and were talking about the situation when Christal said, "Mommy".

I did not answer Christal right away so she placed her hand on my cheek and turned my face toward her and said again "Mommy".

My mother and I were so startled by what she had done to get my attention that we just burst out laughing. It was just like Christal to get what she wanted, when she wanted it.

The nurses at the hospital put Christal immediately in a cold bath with ice. She did not like this one bit, but they had to get her fever down quickly. She had already been given more children's Tylenol. They also needed to take blood and urine specimens to rule out infections. It was obvious to me that Christal would be spending the night at the hospital when they put the IV into her arm. Christal was only one year old. It hurt to see her going through pain again. Life doesn't seem fair when my one-year-old child had already experienced more pain than most people do in a lifetime. But there was nothing I could do to stop it. She just looked up at me and cried. She wanted my protection. She just didn't understand.

I stayed with her in the hospital that night. The next day Dr. Brown informed us that Christal's problem was the result of bacteria in her blood. He did not understand how she got it because this particular bacterium was not related in any way to her kidneys.

Christal had been having frequent bladder infections, for which she took medication. So the logical solution would have been a kidney infection. However, this bacterium was not related in any way to the kidney.

Dr. Brown released Christal from the hospital, but kept her as an outpatient. We would have to come to the hospital every eight hours to get a shot, for the next week.

One afternoon, while waiting in the emergency room for Christal's shot, a car came screeching up to the emergency room doors and a young woman jumped out carrying a baby.

"Someone help my baby", she screamed!

The emergency personnel took the baby to a room and started to work on him. Meanwhile the receptionist called Dr. Brown over. Moments later

Dr. Brown came running into the emergency room where he was escorted to the room where the baby was. It seemed like he was in there for at least a half an hour when he came out and asked the mother to come into another room. After the chaplain arrived there he told her that her baby was dead. He had choked to death while she fed him, she didn't know life saving procedures, and they lived over a half hour from the hospital. It was too late before they even reached the hospital. How sad for this young mother. I once again thanked the Lord to be blessed with my children, and said a prayer for the family of that little boy.

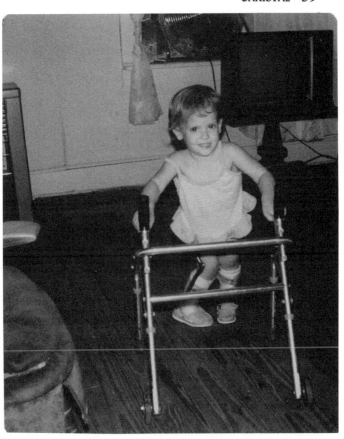

4. Christal, twenty one months old, learning to walk.

10. Physical Therapy
LEARNING TO WALK

Christal learned to walk at the age of twelve months with the aid of a child-sized walker. She would continue to use the walker until she was two. With the walker she could walk throughout the house freely, as long as nothing was in her way. I had often thought of putting handrails down the hallway to help her move about, but as she grew I realized that she did not need a lot of help. She was and still is a determined little girl. To give her too much help would only restrict her in years to come.

When she turned two we were asked to take her to a Physical Therapist for weekly help. Her therapist's name was Laura.

Laura was a pretty young woman. She had shoulder length brown hair and an olive complexion. She had a petite frame, and her personality was perfect for Christal, headstrong and demanding.

She took her job very seriously and was very demanding of Christal. At times I thought she was a little too harsh, if not mean. She would not put up with whining or arguing. If Christal didn't want to do something, she would just tell her that she wasn't leaving until she did.

Christal was old enough to get rid of the walker, Laura had said. It was time to learn how to use a different kind of walking appliance, called loft strands.

Loft strands looked a lot like crutches except that they did not reach to the armpit. Instead, they cupped the arm just above the elbow. It would take a good deal of practice to be able to balance, and coordinate the body on loft strands before Christal would successfully be able to walk with the loft strands. Christal didn't want anything to do with them.

She was comfortable using her walker, and was able to maneuver it just about anywhere. Having to learn how to walk all over again on a new device was just not in her plans. I could see that Laura had her work cut out for her, and I wasn't sure who was going to win this battle. Laura somehow had to get Christal to see that the loft strands would give her even more freedom of movement than the walker.

On one occasion, after we had been there for almost an hour Christal took her first steps by herself with the loft strands. She had been telling Laura that she was tired and wanted to go home; she didn't want to walk, but Laura would not let her. I almost stopped the whole session and took her home myself. After all, I reasoned, she's only two. But something stopped me. I felt like I was watching a television show, just an observer. I had to see the outcome. Had I disassociated myself to Christal's needs? What kind of a mother was I? And then she walked. And I cried.

I learned a valuable lesson. Sometimes you have to let your children experience the work it takes to run the race, so that they can enjoy the reward of their labor.

Laura would be added to the list of people that our family will forever thank and remember.

5. Christal standing on her own.

11. Preschool
PRIVILEGES

Freedom of movement has its privileges. For Christal this was also true. When Christal turned three we placed her in a Christian preschool. We wanted her to be around other children her age, and we wanted it to be in a Christian environment.

Christal's teacher was very attentive to her needs; she always helped Christal maneuver the stairs and other playground equipment. But, I knew I had my work cut out for me in educating the adults on how to treat Christal.

Christal was so cute and petite that the natural instinct to nurture and protect her and treat her special was too much to overcome for most adults. I found myself quite often asking an adult to please treat Christal like a normal child. I remembered the Spina Bifida Coordinator who counseled her father and me on her birth defect when she was born telling us to treat her like a normal child.

"The only thing worse than raising a child with a birth defect" she had said, "was to raise a spoiled child with a birth defect".

Her father and I had no problem with this, but we would continue to educate others of this fact as she grew.

On one occasion as I was taking Christal to her classroom another parent stopped us, or rather Christal, and started talking to her as if she was a baby, a hurt baby. Christal didn't recognize sympathy at that age; she just soaked up the attention. I later asked the parent not to treat her special, not any more special than she would treat any other child. I know this probably sounds a little hard. But I have a child who is just as dear to God as any other but not more. She deserves to be treated equal to others but not above them. Other children resent the favoritism. Especially when they see how capable Christal is.

6. Christal, four years old.

12. Stranded
FLAT TIRE ON I-75

Christal's therapy sessions were close to ending. She did not need help exercising any more because she was getting plenty of exercise walking. During the last month Christal's Therapist asked me if they could put Christal's picture and an article about her in the doctor's journal that they put out each month. They chose Christal because of the progress that she had made in such a short time. I thought it was a great idea, Christal had earned this, and it would be "neat" to see her picture and an article about her in the journal.

We were to be at the Therapist office the next week at ten thirty in the morning for the picture. They had already written the article and just needed her picture to put with it. This journal circulated all over Florida.

The morning of the appointment I dressed Christal in her prettiest dress and fixed her hair in a barrette. Her hair was baby fine and was short; the medicine that she had been taking all her life left her hair brittle and dry, so we kept it short.

The therapist office was in Lake City, thirty miles away. We would take the interstate to get there. We were about half the way there when the tire on my car went flat. It looked like we would probably be late. I hoped that we would still make it in time.

I had never changed a tire before, but it looked like I was about to learn. I had watched Tom do it and felt sure that I would be able to.

I first got out the spare tire and tire jack. Next I placed the jack under the car right by the tire. Then I jacked up the car. Everything seemed to be working so I grabbed the tire iron; Christal was in her car seat buckled in, so I knew she would not be able to get on the highway.

I placed the tire iron on the nut and the wheel moved. I realized then that the nuts had to be loosened before you jack up the car. So I started to let the car down. That was when it happened. The whole car just fell down. The jack had not been positioned properly and had slipped out. I had not put on the emergency brake either, but we were not on a hill, thank God. Moments earlier I had been partially under the car, if I had been hurt, what would have happened to us? I started to cry.

After the car fell, it scared me so badly that I was afraid to try again. I was shaking all over. I looked up ahead in the distance, about thirty yards away was an emergency road phone, but there were a couple of rough looking men at it, and their van was parked in front of it. They were looking in our direction. I prayed to God to help me know what to do. Should I walk to the phone and take a chance that they were OK? I decided to go to the phone and trust that God would take care of us. I wiped my eyes and choked down my tears.

Just as we were walking to the phone, a business man pulled up in a very nice car and asked me if he could drive us somewhere, he said that "we should not be walking down the interstate, it was too dangerous".

I had to make a decision; I had to trust someone for help. This man seemed like the lesser of what could be two evils. We got in his car. I could tell that he was a businessman, his briefcase laid open on the passenger's seat. He moved it so I could sit down, and asked me where we were going and if he could take us there.

I did not want to bother him more than we already had so I told him he could take us to the next exit, Lake City, and I could call my husband from the gas station right there.

I had told him about Christal's appointment with the therapist and he was willing to take us there, but I did not feel comfortable bothering him. So we waited until Tom got to the station. He had already changed the tire and just needed to pick us up on the way and drop us off at the car. But by the time that he had finished we had missed the appointment. They still put the article in the journal but without a picture.

13. The H.R.S
CHILD NEGLECT

Before Christal turned four, her father and I divorced. The children and I moved south to a town called Bradenton, in order to be closer to my parents. I needed their emotional support and guidance.

When we moved, we took with us a camper that had belonged to my father, and parked it in a campground for the first two months. It was cramped, and we needed a home, so two months after we arrived in Bradenton, we rented a duplex.

I began work right away on the night shift, and also checked Christal into the county clinic so that she could continue her regular appointments.

One of the attendants who worked at the clinic asked me if Christal could benefit from physical therapy. "It's offered free from the state", she had said.

All that was needed was for me to make an appointment for Christal to be evaluated by their team of professionals to see if she might qualify. I made the appointment for the following month.

One month later my hours changed at work and I was put on the day shift. It was not a good idea to make any waves at my job this early on; I was already under a lot of tension working in a "man's" job. My boss had let me know in many ways. So, I called the clinic and let them know that we would be missing the appointment and would have to reschedule.

The next day an H.R.S. caseworker showed up at my door. She had a complaint of "gross child neglect", Christal being the child and I being the parent.

The Children's medical services had turned me in for missing Christal's appointment, a voluntary evaluation that I had made the month earlier. They had stated that Christal was a child with a severe birth defect, and that I had never taken her to see a doctor.

The caseworker took both of my daughters into another room and questioned them, not about neglect, but about abuse. She asked them if anyone ever touched them in private areas, she asked them if we ever beat them. They must have been so confused to have a complete stranger take them away to a separate room and question them like this. I was angry and disgusted to think that an agency within the state would not do their homework well enough to realize that Christal could not have lived without having seen a doctor at birth.

I was later informed that they had decided that I had not neglected my children, because "my house was clean".

But, they would keep me on probation for a period of one year. What would have happened if my house had been dirty? I wondered.

14. Evaluation
SPECIAL TESTING

I rescheduled another appointment with the clinic to have Christal evaluated, and this time we were sure not to miss the appointment.

Christal was to be seen by four different doctors, a neurologist, a physical therapist, an occupational therapist, and a pediatrician.

We were used to the tests the neurologist was performing. He measured her head, checked her eyes, her shunt, and the surgery on her back. She was in excellent condition for a Spina Bifida child.

The physical therapist's tests were also a repeat of the tests other physical therapists had performed on Christal. She also recommended that Christal did not need any extra physical therapy provided by the state.

The occupational therapist's tests, however, were completely new to us. She tested Christal's emotional and mental level. She found Christal to be advanced in language and speech skills, and a little slow in math skills. She also described Christal's disposition to a tee. I did not need a doctor to tell me that Christal was "an attractive petite little girl who could sometimes use her cuteness to manipulate others into doing what she wanted", but it was interesting to hear what I already knew from a perfect stranger, who only questioned Christal for about thirty minutes.

The pediatrician was last, and he was routine.

We were given a formal report on the committee's decision regarding whether on not Christal would be entitled to some extra physical therapy. They had found that she did not require any extra help, so none was given. However, they did believe she was ready to start Kindergarten even though she would not turn five until the sixteenth of September. Sixteen days too late in the state of Florida at that time.

15. Shriner's Hospital
SPECIAL PEOPLE

It always took me longer to get through the checkouts at the grocery store when I brought Christal with me. Someone was sure to start up a conversation with Christal or me no matter where we were.

On one occasion, while we were at the grocery store, an elderly man who was bagging our groceries started talking to me about Christal. He wanted to know what she had and where she was going for treatment.

I thought his latest inquiry a little unusual but answered it anyway.

He informed me that he was a Shriner, a member of the Mason's organization. I had no clue as to just what a Shriner was at that time; so he went on to explain about the Shriner's Hospital for Crippled Children in Tampa.

He said we could qualify for help from this Hospital, and all that was needed was for us to be evaluated to be sure we qualified. He gave me his card.

Later that evening I called him, and set up an appointment. He came out to our house the following week and had me sign papers, and he checked the medical papers I had on Christal. She qualified.

We were given an appointment to attend a clinical evaluation for Spina Bifida Children. It was here that we met some of the most wonderful people we know.

The Shriners, a group of men throughout the world who are part of the Mason organization, fund this Hospital. One of their main goals is to help crippled children.

Upon arrival Christal and I were taken into an examination room. It was here that we met Jackie Frost, the Spina Bifida Coordinator for the hospital. She told us that we would see four different types of doctors and a few nurses. After they had gathered all the information from their check up with Christal they would sit down together and decide the best route to go for Christal's health.

The first doctor we met was Doctor Gudera, an orthopedic doctor. He did not like the way Christal was walking. She seemed to limp as if one leg was growing longer than the other. After having x-rays taken of her legs he informed me that Christal's one hip was continually out of the socket and would stay that way, but the other slipped in and out. Both of her hips needed to be doing the same thing to keep her legs growing the same. If both hips did not stay in or out of the sockets then he would have to operate. He wanted to check her progress in another six months. He also put in an order for Christal to have new leg braces, since the ones she was wearing were too small. Her left leg also turned in when she walked, so he kept her in a reciprocal brace intended to keep her legs positioned correctly. This brace had a band around her waist, which connected to cables at her hips, which also connected to her lower leg braces or AFO's. The cables kept her lower leg braces positioned correctly. Christal didn't like this brace, as usual, because it restricted her freedom of movement. But it would teach her how to hold her legs correctly.

The next doctor that examined Christal was the Urologist, Dr. Hoover. He was a small man with reddish blond hair, and he looked to be about forty years old. He was also very much a gentleman. Christal liked him immediately.

Dr. Hoover's nurse took a urine sample from Christal to be tested for bacteria. Christal had frequent bladder infections, and Dr. Hoover wanted to put her on medication to keep them under control. He put her on a drug which would thicken and strengthen the bladder, this would help the bladder to keep its balloon shape in order not to pocket urine. He also put her on a drug to fight against infection in the bladder and urinary tract. This was all an effort to avoid the possibility of hurting her kidneys. If her bladder became too full, the urine could back up into the kidneys and cause serious kidney problems. She could live without her bladder, but she could not live without her kidneys.

We were also visited by a neurosurgeon who measured Christal's head, checked her shunt, and looked at the surgery on her back. He asked us if Christal was having any problems with her shunt and I said no. He could tell from the x-ray taken that there was plenty of shunt left laying in her stomach cavity for growth, and he gave her his OK.

After a routine visit by the pediatrician Christal was sent to the brace shop on the first floor, to be fitted to new leg braces, which would have the new reciprocal brace attached to them.

The man in the brace shop put casts on both of Christal's legs from the knee down. Then he cut the casts off. He would use these casts to make molds of Christal's legs, which would be used to make the Leg braces. He also took measurements for the new brace. It would take two weeks for the brace shop to make Christal's brace, and then Christal would have to be fitted to it.

Two weeks later Christal put her new brace on for the first time. She did not like it. It was hard for her to walk. In fact, she would have to learn how to walk all over again. Dr. Gudera had to check the fit of the brace before we could go home, and he gave his OK.

16. Peace Lutheran School
KINDERGARTEN

Christal started kindergarten just before her sixth birthday. She was the smallest child in the school at that time. Equipped with her loft strands, she was ready to face the world, or at least she thought she was.

Ambulating was not a problem. Christal was able to do almost anything other children did. She used her upper body to compensate for the weakness in her legs. And she was well liked among the other children in the school, who seemed to enjoy including her in on the fun.

Her personality was so alive and friendly that it became a problem as she realized that she could use her shortcomings to manipulate others around her including adults.

The pastor of our church told me once that Christal gave the other children an opportunity to understand the blessings of serving others. Had she not been in the school, the other children might never know how to react to a person with disabilities.

17. Kidney Problems
DIFFICULT PHASE

Orthopedically, Christal was doing great! But as she began school, we entered into the most difficult phase of her birth defect so far, her kidneys and her bladder.

Because of the loss of feeling in her bladder, Christal was prone to frequent bladder infections, which sometimes resulted in kidney infections. When she was in the first grade, Christal had to be hospitalized for a kidney infection. She spiked an immediate temperature of one hundred and six, and became very lethargic. After a week of hospitalization she finally recovered. Her class made her a cake and brought it to the hospital. She was in all her glory.

Shortly after this visit to the hospital, Christal had to be seen in the Spina Bifida Clinic at the Shriners hospital. It was then that her urologist, Dr. Hoover decided that she needed to start using catheters to help her bladder rid itself of waste. I was shown how to insert the catheter, and was told this needed to be done a minimum of four times during the day. The problem was, though, I had to work, and my job as a manager was very demanding. I could catherize Christal in the morning before I left for work, immediately after I came home from work, and before she went to bed, but who would do it while she was in school?

The ideal answer was to have Christal learn, and she was trying, but she was so tiny that it was impossible for her to balance herself on the toilet and insert a catheter at the same time. So her teacher and I came up with the idea of letting the eighth grade girls catheterize her this one time during the day. They did not object to this idea, and they wanted to help her. As I look back on this, I realize the love they must have had for Christal. God certainly has blessed her.

18. Ballet
LEARNING TO DANCE

Christal wanted to take ballet lessons, but her lower legs had few muscles that worked in them, and her feet barely moved at all. I wondered how she would be able to perform. But her desire was strong; she wanted to be like the other girls, she wanted to be like her sister.

Elizabeth had taken ballet when we had lived in Live Oak, and so after I was able to afford it, she continued with jazz in Bradenton. I inquired about ballet for Christal, and the instructor was more than happy to accommodate. He taught the beginning classes. Christal would be a beginner.

She loved the practices, and used her loft strands to help balance. She practiced all the steps and moves that she had learned at home every day. She really became just as good as the other children in her group. They had to practice because at the end of the year they would get to dance in the county's theater, the Van Weisel.

Finally, the night of the dance recital had arrived. I had previously purchased tickets for the best seats in the theater, right up front. My new husband, Dave, and my parents accompanied me.

Christal was still wearing diapers, because she had no control over her bowels or her bladder. She could feel when she was wet, she just couldn't stop it from happening. It had been a much longer day than I had expected, and unfortunately I did not pack enough diapers. Christal had been drinking a lot of liquids as well. This was a bad combination as diapers are not leak-proof for older children. Christal was seven years old.   Just before the recital started, Elizabeth came down into the audience and found me.

"Christal needs you, mom" she said. "Her diaper is leaking".

I left my seat and followed Elizabeth, but was stopped by an attendant who informed me that it was very unprofessional to walk on the stage just before the performance.

I did not bother explaining. There was no time anyway. Later I thought about how insignificant a little thing like walking on the stage was compared to what Christal was probably going through.

Christal told me that her "diaper had leaked and did I have another?"

"No", I said. I had forgot to pack any, I was sorry. I assured her that she would be OK. That no one would know. Her group was one of the first to dance anyway. I tried to reassure her that everything would be OK. And then I went back to my seat, the correct way.

Christal's group was not first. But when she came out on the stage you could have heard a pin drop in the theater. She walked out with her loft strands and took her position. She danced every step perfectly, I was very proud of her. After the dance was over the audience would not stop clapping. I had a lump in my throat and was trying hard to choke back the tears. I could see that my mom was also crying.

As Christal's group left the stage I could see a little puddle where Christal had sat when her dance had finished. I felt bad for the next group. No one ever said anything about it though.

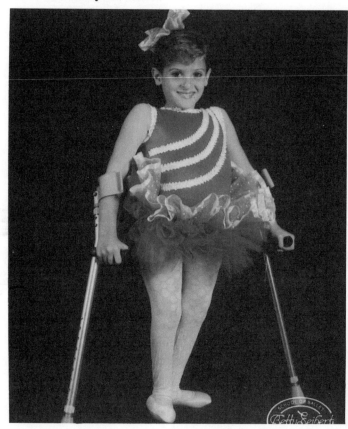

7. Christal, eight years old, at Dance Recital.

19. Mistake
THE APPENDIX

Christal was seeing a pediatrician in Bradenton who also had a child with a birth defect. At first he would not take any more patients, but because I listed him as our pediatrician when my son David was born a year earlier, he also saw my other two children.

He was an excellent Doctor and we liked him a lot. But one of his other two associates didn't seem as skilled.

At normal checkups you could request the doctor of your choice, and this was OK. But on the frequent times that Christal got sick with urinary tract infections, we almost always saw the other doctor.

He was new at being a pediatrician. He looked to be in his late twenties. And it was my opinion that he was just too "gung-ho", too quick to put you in the hospital for the slightest thing. This happened so often to us that I began to wonder if he was supporting the hospital.

Once, he put my oldest child in the hospital to have her appendix removed. It turned out that she only had gastritis. Thank God for a questioning surgeon!

But Christal was not so lucky. I was at work when it happened, and of course it happened during an off time, "Murphy's law". She spiked a fever of one hundred and six and became tired and listless. After getting Christal's fever down to a safer degree, I called the doctor's office. I felt sure it was a kidney infection. The doctor wanted to check Christal there. He barely examined her, only checking her abdomen and asking her if it hurt when he touched. He felt sure it was an acute appendicitis. Christal said it hurt in her back all the time, and even after I told him I felt sure it was another kidney infection, because she had the same symptoms (immediate high fever, pain in her back, strong urine smell), he still wanted to remove her appendix, never checking for a kidney infection. He sent us immediately to the hospital and scheduled an operation for two 2 A.M. the next morning.

Later that next day the pediatrician came to Christal's room to see how she was doing. He informed me that the surgeon did not find anything wrong with Christal's appendix, but they would be sending it down to pathology for testing. He also had the nurse get a urine sample from Christal, and they would start treating her for a kidney infection.

I was so angry with this man, but I did not say anything to him. He had Christal's appendix removed for nothing! And especially after I had urged him to check for a kidney infection. He had operated on her appendix when both of her kidneys were sick.

A week later as Christal was still recovering from the kidney infection, the pediatrician came into her room to check on her. He told me "pathology had found a mark on the appendix, so eventually it would have had to be removed anyway".

When I look back on this event, it's almost comical that I allowed this man to remove my child's appendix while neglecting what was wrong. And I not only paid for it, I also got to pay for the research it took to cover this doctor's behind. In the future I would not allow anyone to scare me into an operation without a second opinion, especially if I believe something else is wrong.

We never went to see this doctor again. Instead, I switched to a regular Medical Doctor, recommended to me by a friend. His name was Doctor Gordon,

and he was well versed on Spina Bifida. He pointed
out some interesting facts that I had never heard
before. He put Christal on vitamin C and told us
what fruits she needed to eat to help her bladder
infection problem. He had done his research before
our office visit, and had copied information for me.
He was more helpful than any of the pediatricians we
had in the past.

20. Sick Kidneys
MAJOR OPERATION

Twice a year Christal would continue to be seen at the Shriners Hospital in Tampa. Every visit required x-rays, urine tests, and sometimes blood tests and special types of x-rays.

Because of Christal's constant bladder infections and the few kidney infections she had experienced, the urologist, Dr. Hoover, decided that an operation on both of Christal's kidneys was necessary to protect the kidneys from future damage.

Christal's bladder frequently backed up and pushed urine back up through the connecting tubes (ureters) to the kidneys. This was the reason she was having kidney infections. Dr. Hoover wanted to disconnect her ureters from the bladder, and implant them into another area of the bladder. Her surgery was scheduled for the earliest possible date, which happened to be a week before Christmas.

Because the Shriners Hospital was not equipped to handle a major surgery, Christal was taken to St.

Joseph's Hospital, also in Tampa. Dr. Hoover would be the surgeon.

I checked Christal in, and stayed with her most of the time. We also put up a small Christmas tree in her room. I was hoping that she would be able to come home before Christmas, but we weren't counting on it.

The next morning, the nurses prepared Christal for surgery. When they took her this time, I was allowed to come and be with her until they put her to sleep.

Christal was hooked up to all types of monitors. I held her hand as the anesthesiologist put a mask over her mouth and nose and told her to count to ten. I could tell she was afraid, and was glad that I was there for her. I fought hard not to cry as she counted. She was so little. Why did she have to go through so much? I would take her place in a heartbeat if God would let me. She fell asleep before she reached ten.

I was escorted out of the room, and was told that the doctor would talk to us as soon as the operation was finished. As hard as I tried to be strong, nothing could stop the flow of tears from my eyes. I cried not out of fear, but out of love. I believed God would take care of Christal; he had left her in very capable hands so far. And I believed He had bigger plans for her, but it still hurt tremendously to watch her go through so much. I prayed for God's help, and wisdom for the doctors who were attending Christal.

After a few hours, the operation was over. Dr. Hoover came to talk to us. The operation was a success, he believed. Christal was in the recovery room and we could see her.

She was not completely conscious when I went in, but she was trying to wake up. She slipped in and out of consciousness and did recognize me, and she was having a hard time focusing her eyes. I was glad to be there for her. Finally, she did regain consciousness and spoke a little. Of course, she didn't remember anything that had happened during the surgery.

After spending almost a week in the Hospital, Christal was released on Christmas Eve. We took her home where she became the center of attention. Christal's operation was definitely a success. She has not had a bladder infection since!

21. Sports
ROLLER SKATING

Christal has never been afraid to try anything that the other children can do. Of all my children she is the one who always wants to fit in with the crowd, wear the latest fashions, and play all the sports.

Like any other child, she learned to ride a bike when she was about five years old. We had to put training wheels on it so she could balance, but she begged to have them removed. She ended up having one training wheel on for balance. She needed this to be able to mount the bike.

Roller-skating was next. Christal used her sister's Fisher Price skates to learn on. I was very apprehensive about this, but have learned that Christal has a good head on her shoulders and will not do anything that she is afraid of. She learned how to roller skate in the driveway and from there she wanted to go to the skating rink. All of her friends were going. She was about eight years old at the time.

The roller skating rink had a much smoother floor than our driveway and the wheels on their skates rolled more freely than the Fisher Price skates. This combined with a sea of children on the rink made me nervous. I didn't want Christal to get hurt, but she was determined. She got out on the floor with her loft strands and started to skate. I followed behind her. Everyone was watching us, which seemed to bother me more than Christal. In fact, I don't think it even bothered Christal. She just soaked up the attention. She became well liked and known in the skating rink by all the people who worked there.

Roller-skating progressed into ice-skating. My father worked in Venice and told us about an ice skating rink there. After much prodding, the children convinced me to take them. We coaxed my son, David, into staying with his grandparents because he was only two at the time, and I knew I would not be able to help him and Christal at the same time.

Little did I know! Christal learned to ice skate easier than she learned to roller skate. But we were not as welcome here as we were at the roller skating rink. One of the attendants brought Christal a walker to use on the ice, and told us about a handicap ice-skating program that they had every Thursday night. Christal used the walker until she felt comfortable, and then she didn't want to be bothered with it. We also joined the handicap ice skating program.

The handicap program met once a week to teach the children how to skate, and to rehearse a special Christmas program that they put on once a year. Christal learned how to do a figure eight and how to skate backward. But most of the children in the program were mentally challenged and Christal felt a little out of place. The other children had the strength to skate, and once they understood what was expected of them, they learned quickly. Christal understood but did not have the control of her legs that they had.

Christal stayed in the handicap program for just over one year. We still returned to skate during regular hours as well.

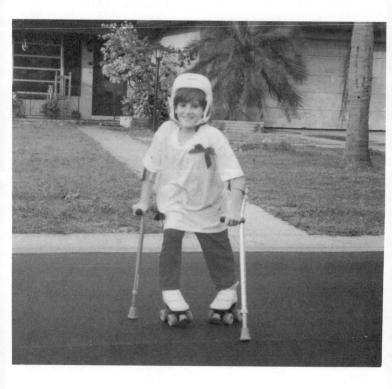

8. Christal, roller skating.

9. Christal (front row, 2nd from left), thirteen years old.

22. Cheerleading
BUILDING PYRAMIDS

When Christal was eleven I let her join the city cheerleading squad. By this time, I learned to let Christal do what she she could do. She knew her limits.

The coaches were happy to have Christal, she started out in a younger group because she was so small and none of the uniforms would fit her in her age group. This worked out for Christal's benefit. It gave Christal time to learn the cheers and the moves. Most of the older girls had been in the program for a few years and knew the cheers, especially the girls in her age group and older.

Cheerleading fit Christal to a tee. She was well liked by all the other girls and quickly learned the cheers and most of the moves. She even learned how to build pyramids.

In Christal's second year as a cheerleader she was picked as the homecoming queen, but was unable to accept it because she was away visiting her father for the weekend, at the time.

10. Christal, twelve years old,
a *real* Cheer Leader.

11. Christal, singing solo at Desoto Square Mall.

Christal is now a junior at Manatee High School in Bradenton, Florida. She excels in English and in Music, loves horses and country music, plays the piano, sings solos at church and plans to be either a pediatrician or a country music singer after she graduates college.

Christal started her first job at 16 and earned enough money to purchase her own car, which she drives regularly with special attachments.

CONCLUSION

T
welve years after Christal was born I finally got an answer to my question. A lack of folic acid during the first six weeks of pregnancy was the reason Christal was born with Spina Bifida.

It all fit together. Just before I became pregnant with Christal, I had gone through an emotionally stressful situation and had lost over ten pounds. This put me fifteen pounds under weight for my height and frame. We had recently moved which also added extra stress. I remember my father even commenting that I looked too thin. I was not healthy enough to become pregnant, and had skipped a few periods. I did not even realize that I was pregnant until a month after conception. Also, I have always had weak blood. With my first child, I was put on Iron immediately. With Christal, the clinic did not start vitamins at all; instead, they wanted me to get the vitamins from the food I ate. I started taking vitamins on my own a few months after I became pregnant. This was too late. I needed to be healthy before I became pregnant. Christal is a beautiful child, and a gift from God. I know that He has watched her and helped her even before she was born, and she has a purpose in this life. I would not trade the past seventeen years with Christal for anything on earth, but if I could change anything I would educate women on the importance of being healthy before they become pregnant.

If you are sexually active, take vitamin B-12. It's that simple. Vitamin B-12 provides folic acid in the diet. Don't wait until you think you're pregnant. It may already be too late for your child.

TERMS

Ambulating:
  To move about
Anesthesiologist:
  A doctor who can deliver drugs to lesson bodily sensations
Bacterium:
  Any of a large group of microscopic plants which may or may not produce disease
Breech:
  Rump or Buttocks, a child bearing delivery where the baby is delivered butt or feet first
Catheter:
  A tube for insertion into a bodily passage or cavity esp. for drawing off material (as urine)
D&C:
  Dilation and Curettage, Dilating the cervix and scraping the uterine wall with a curette, to clean the uterine wall
Forceps:
  A hand-held instrument for grasping, holding, or pulling objects esp. for delicate operations

HRS:
>   Health and Rehabilitative Services; an organization which among many other things, looks out for the welfare of Children in the State of Florida

Hydrocephalus:
>   Abnormal increase in the amount of fluid in the cranial cavity accompanied by expansion of the ventricles, enlargement of the skull, and atrophy of the brain

IV:
>   Intravenous, within or injected into a vein

Neurologist:
>   A doctor who specializes in the treatment of the nervous system

NICU:
>   (Neo-natal Intensive Care Unit) Area of a hospital, which specializes in the intense treatment of newborns with serious problems

Obstetrician:
>   A doctor who specializes in childbirth

Occupational Therapist:
>   A therapist who prescribes creative activity for therapy

Orthopedics:
>   The correction or prevention of skeletal deformities

Parapodium:
>   A free standing brace which holds the hip bones in their sockets

Pediatric Neurosurgeon:
>   A surgeon who specializes in child nervous systems

Pediatrician:
>   A doctor who specializes in children

Reciprocal Brace:
>   Leg braces which are held in place by cables attached at the waist

Shunt:
>   A pump which reroutes spinal fluid at the brain to keep it from building up pressure

Spina Bifida:
>   A birth defect where the spine does not close completely during development

Spinal Meningitis:
>   An infection in the spinal fluid

Ureters:
>   Tubes which connect the kidneys to the bladder

Ventricular Fluid:
>   Fluid which lubricates the brain and spinal cord